THE POP PIANO PLAYER

MAMMA MIA

... AND 13 OTHER CLASSIC POP SONGS

ARRANGED AND PERFORMED BY JOHN KEMBER

FABER *ff* MUSIC

CONTENTS

© 2009 by Faber Music Ltd
This edition first published in 2009
Bloomsbury House 74–77 Great Russell Street London WC1B 3DA
Music processed by Jackie Leigh
Cover design by Lydia Merrills-Ashcroft
CD recorded and produced by Porcupine Studios
Printed in England by Caligraving Ltd
All rights reserved

ISBN10: 0-571-53297-7
EAN13: 978-0-571-53297-1

To buy Faber Music publications or to find out about the full range of titles available
please contact your local music retailer or Faber Music sales enquiries:

Faber Music Ltd, Burnt Mill, Elizabeth Way, Harlow CM20 2HX
Tel: +44 (0) 1279 82 89 82   Fax: +44 (0) 1279 82 89 83
sales@fabermusic.com   fabermusic.com

PREFACE

The *Pop Piano Player* books aim to help pianists understand and play a
selection of the greatest pop songs so that they are truly 'under their fingers'.
The pieces in this book span almost five decades of popular music, representing styles
from the 60's to the present day and from musicians from both sides of the Atlantic.

Each piece is presented in two formats, which gives both the basic chord structure
and symbols as well as a piano arrangement of each song. By learning the changes,
the chords will become familiar, the progressions more readily understood and the
shapes will lie more comfortably under the hands. More information on how to interpret
and voice the chords is given on *page 64*.

The first version of each song gives the melody, lyrics and chord symbols in its
standard key. Lyrics are given so that the character of each song is understood,
but all verses are not always given, depending on the length and complexity of the song.
The chord symbols enable pianists to accompany singers and instrumentalists, creating
their own style of accompaniment. This format ultimately gives pianists the foundation
on which to develop personal interpretation and improvisation.

The arrangements for solo piano which follow keep largely to the same chord patterns
though with some changes to the overall structure regarding verses etc., to create
a balanced piano solo. These solos I have recorded on the accompanying CD.

John Kember

ALWAYS ON MY MIND
(MELODY, LYRICS AND CHORD CHANGES)

Words and Music by Johnny Christopher,
Wayne Thompson and Mark James

TRACK 1

ALWAYS ON MY MIND

(SOLO ARRANGEMENT)

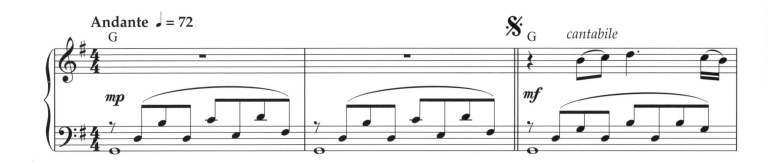

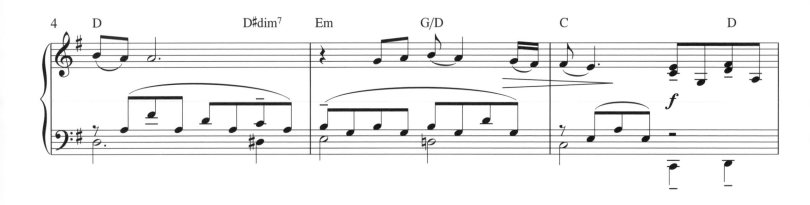

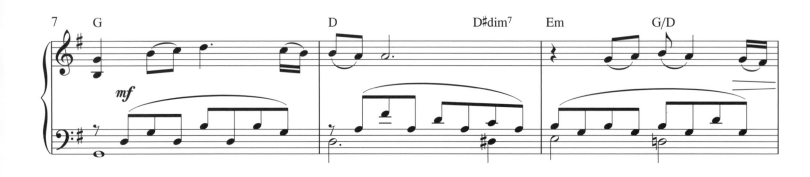

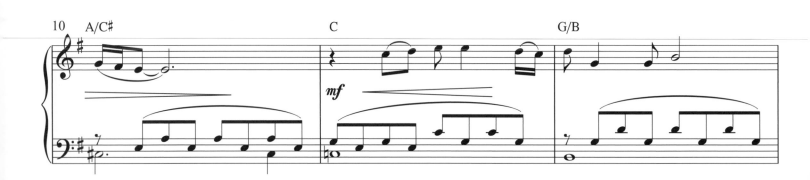

SEE THE DAY
(MELODY, LYRICS AND CHORD CHANGES)

Words and Music by
Dee C Lee

SEE THE DAY
(SOLO ARRANGEMENT)

BEING WITH YOU

(MELODY, LYRICS AND CHORD CHANGES)

Words and Music by
William Robinson

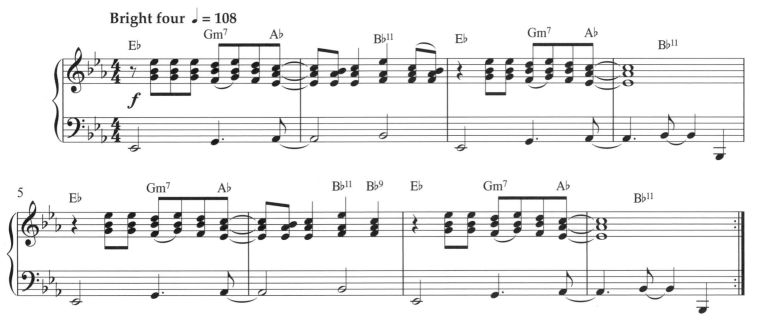

BEING WITH YOU

(SOLO ARRANGEMENT)

TRACK 3

WHITE FLAG
(MELODY, LYRICS AND CHORD CHANGES)

Words and Music by Dido Armstrong,
Rick Nowels and Rollo Armstrong

WHITE FLAG
(SOLO ARRANGEMENT)

Slow ballad tempo ♩ = 80

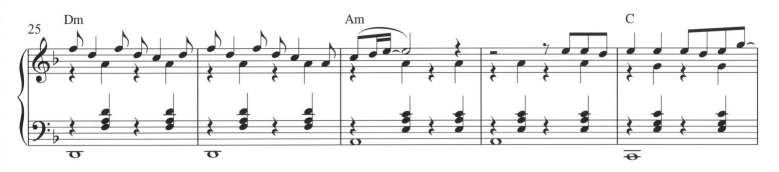

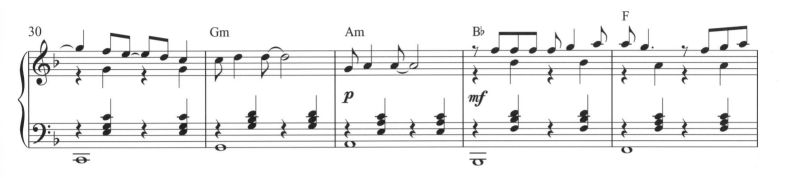

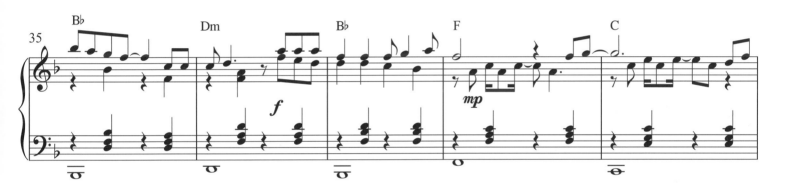

MAMMA MIA

(MELODY, LYRICS AND CHORD CHANGES)

Words and Music by Benny Andersson,
Björn Ulvaeus and Stig Anderson

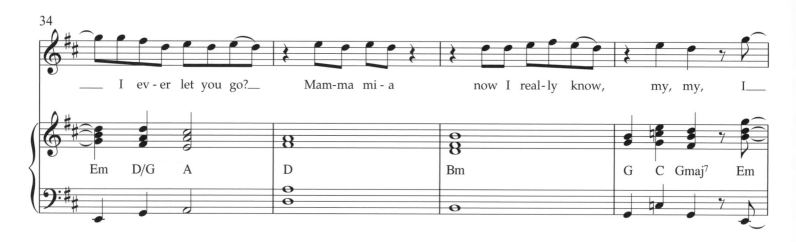

MAMMA MIA
(SOLO ARRANGEMENT)

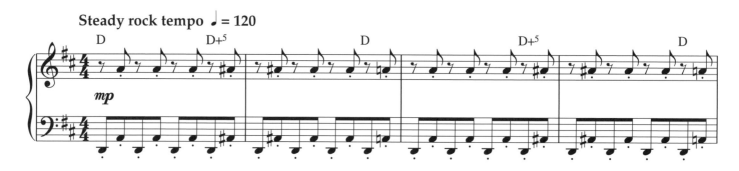

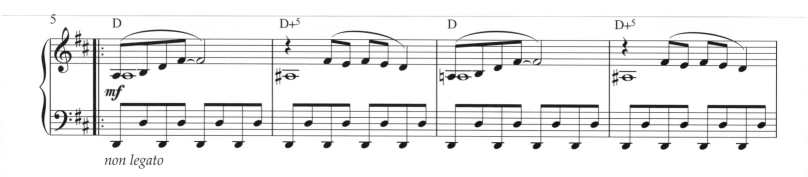

FROM BOTH SIDES NOW

(MELODY, LYRICS AND CHORD CHANGES)

Words and Music by
Joni Mitchell

26

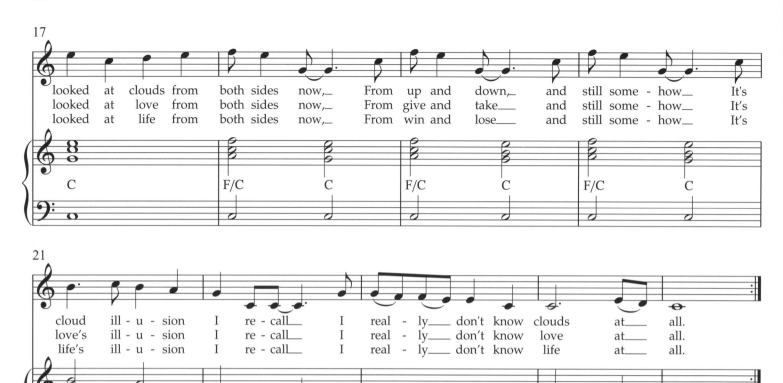

TRACK 6

FROM BOTH SIDES NOW
(SOLO ARRANGEMENT)

SOMEWHERE

(MELODY, LYRICS AND CHORD CHANGES)

Words and Music by
Eva Cassidy and Chris Biondo

SOMEWHERE

(SOLO ARRANGEMENT)

I DON'T FEEL LIKE DANCIN'
(MELODY, LYRICS AND CHORD CHANGES)

Words and Music by Scott Hoffman,
Jason Sellards and Elton John

no danc-in' to-day. I don't feel like danc-in', danc-in', E-ven if I find no-thing bet-ter to do._ Don't feel like

danc - in', danc - in', Why'd you pick a tune when I'm not__ in the mood? Don't feel like

TRACK 8

I DON'T FEEL LIKE DANCIN'
(SOLO ARRANGEMENT)

Steady rock beat ♩ = 88

HOTEL CALIFORNIA
(MELODY, LYRICS AND CHORD CHANGES)

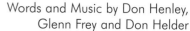

Words and Music by Don Henley,
Glenn Frey and Don Helder

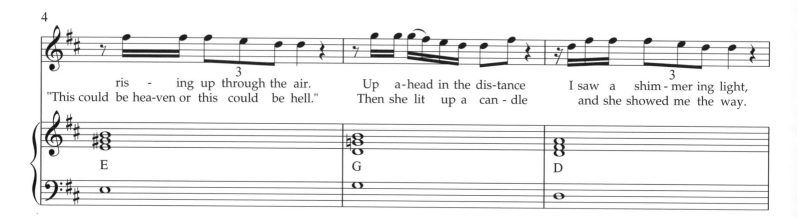

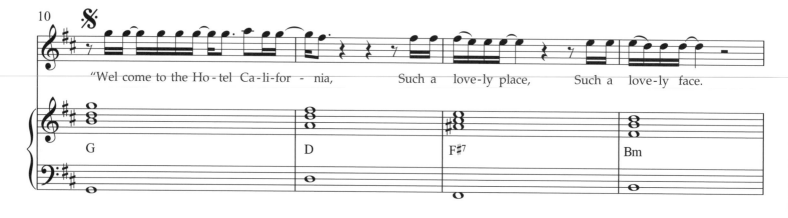

CODA

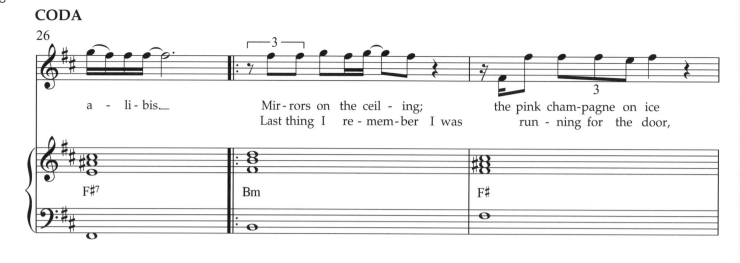

a - li - bis.___
Last thing I re - mem - ber I was

Mir - rors on the ceil - ing;
run - ning for the door,

the pink cham-pagne on ice

F#7   Bm   F#

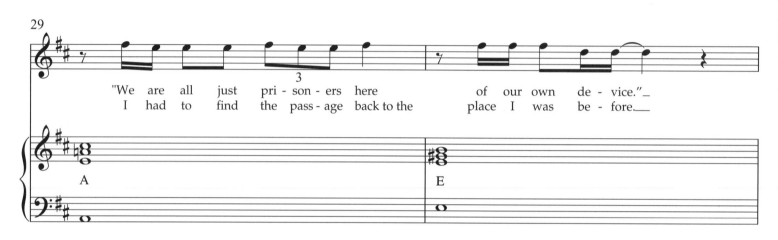

"We are all just pri - son - ers here
I had to find the pass - age back to the

of our own de - vice."___
place I was be - fore.___

A   E

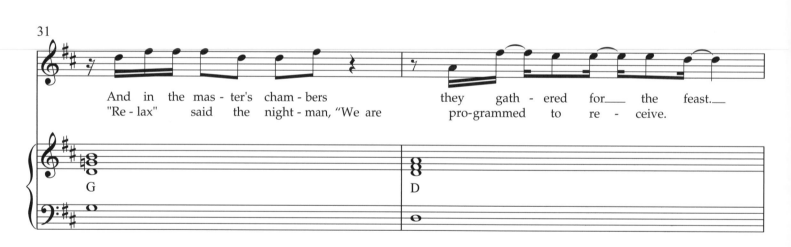

And in the mas - ter's cham - bers
"Re - lax" said the night - man, "We are

they gath - ered for___ the feast.___
pro - grammed to re - ceive.

G   D

Repeat to fade

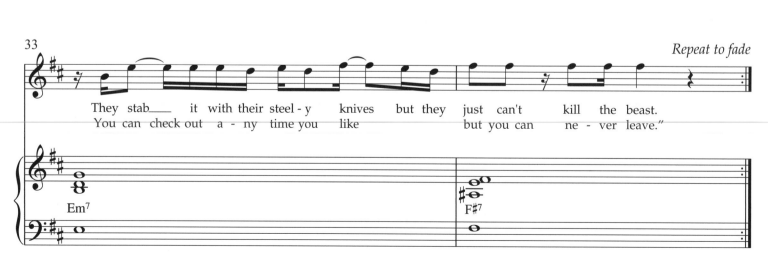

They stab___ it with their steel - y knives but they just can't kill the beast.
You can check out a - ny time you like but you can ne - ver leave."

Em7   F#7

HOTEL CALIFORNIA
(SOLO ARRANGEMENT)

FOR YOUR EYES ONLY
(MELODY, LYRICS AND CHORD CHANGES)

Words by Mick Leeson
Music by Bill Conti

2nd time to Coda ⊕

18
on-ly for you.___ The love I know you need in me, the fan-ta-sy you've freed in me.
The pas-sions that col-lide in me, the wild a-ban-doned side of me.

Gmaj7 Em7 C Am7 G/B Em7

21
On-ly for you,_____ on-ly for you.___ For

C/D G

CODA

27
On-ly for you,_____ for your eyes on-ly._____

C/D Am7/D G

TRACK ⑩

FOR YOUR EYES ONLY
(SOLO ARRANGEMENT)

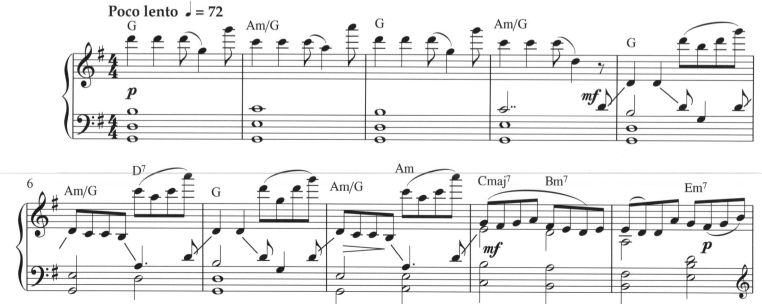

Poco lento ♩ = 72

G Am/G G Am/G G

p *mf*

6
Am/G D7 G Am/G Am Cmaj7 Bm7 Em7

mf *p*

VALERIE
(MELODY, LYRICS AND CHORD CHANGES)

Words and Music by Dave McCabe,
Sean Payne, Abigail Harding,
Boyan Chowdhury and Russell Pritchard

-rie._____ Why don't you come on o - ver Va - le - rie?_____

VALERIE
(SOLO ARRANGEMENT)

First time D.%
Second time repeat and fade

YOU'RE BEAUTIFUL
(MELODY, LYRICS AND CHORD CHANGES)

Words and Music by James Blunt,
Sacha Skarbek and Amanda Ghost

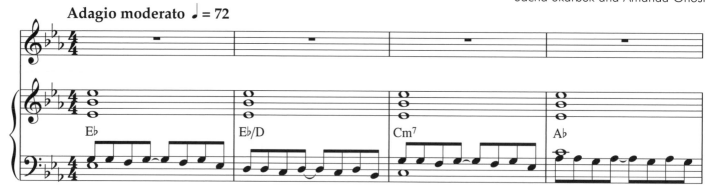

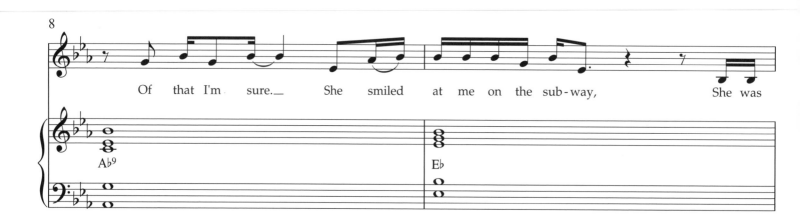

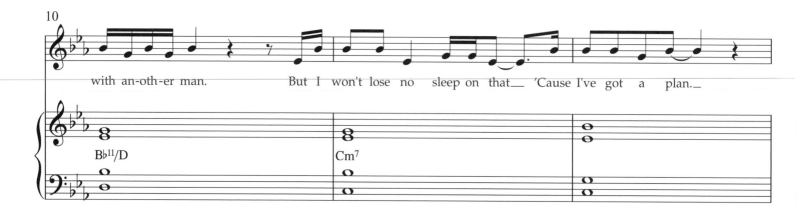

You're beau-ti - ful.___ You're beau-ti - ful.___ You're beau-ti - ful,___ it's___

true. I saw___ your face in a crowd-ed___ place,___ And I

don't know what__ to__ do___ 'Cause I'll ne - ver__ be__ with you.___

TRACK 12

YOU'RE BEAUTIFUL
(SOLO ARRANGEMENT)

Adagio moderato ♩ = 72

JESUS TO A CHILD
(MELODY, LYRICS AND CHORD CHANGES)

Words and Music by
George Michael

JESUS TO A CHILD
(SOLO ARRANGEMENT)

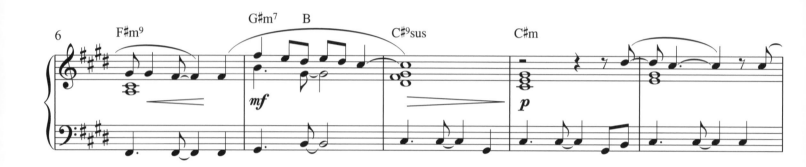

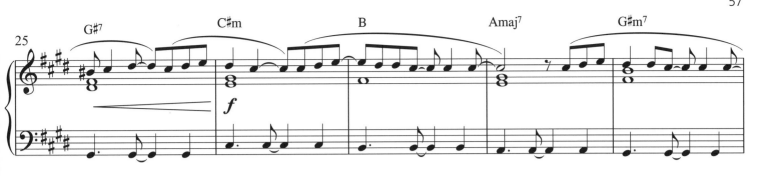

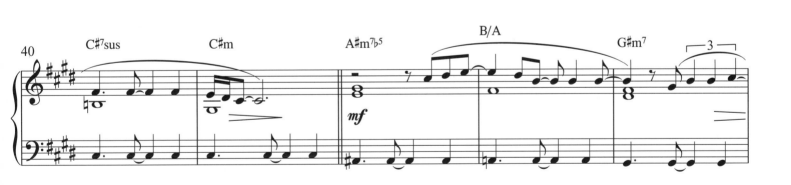

EASY
(MELODY, LYRICS AND CHORD CHANGES)

Words and Music by
Lionel Richie

CODA

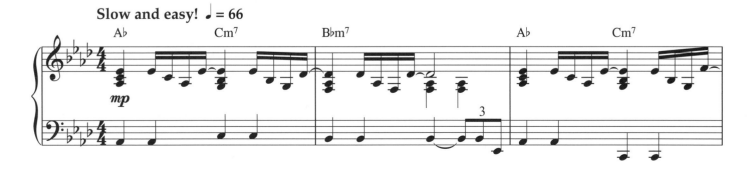

EASY
(SOLO ARRANGEMENT)

A CHORD GUIDE FOR POP PIANISTS

Chords in popular music tend to be mainly root based – so a chord of C major will have C as its bass (lowest note), and the 3rd and 5th notes of the scale make up the rest of the chord. The chords in pop songs are likely to revolve around just a few chosen chords, generally with one chord per bar, and frequently have a familiar or repetitive pattern. These have often been developed from the guitar rather than the keyboard.

- **Major and minor tonalities:** plain symbols such as G, D, and A denote a major chord. Minor chords are symbolised by a small 'm' as in Gm, Dm and Am. **Additional notes** can be added and are referred to as the note number above the root, such as 6th, 7th, 9th, 11th and 13th.

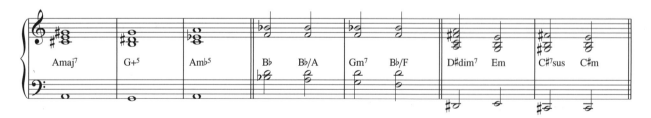

- The major 7th uses the seventh note of the scale named by the chord, so Dmaj7 would have a C♯. D^7 implies a **minor seventh** so would have a C♮.

- The 5th **can be augmented** (enlarged) by a semitone which is indicated by a ♯ or + sign, or **diminished** (reduced) by a semitone, indicated by the ♭ or – sign.

- 9^{ths}, 11^{ths} **and** 13^{ths} can be augmented or diminished in the same way.

- **Inverted chords** (where the bass note is other than the root) are indicated as F/A, an F major chord over an A bass, or Am/D, an A minor chord over a D bass.

- The diminished 7th (dim^7) is made up of minor 3rd intervals to make a chord that is distinctive in tone and often used as a chromatic link between chords. The **half-diminished chord** is shown as $Em^{7♭5}$ and is best thought of as Gm/E. *Always on my Mind* shows the chromatic use of the diminished 7th chord.

- The **suspended chord** (Fsus4, or just Fsus) has a fourth intending to resolve onto the third, and as such has no tonality until it does so.